Specific Skill Series

Using the Context

Richard A. Boning

Fifth Edition

SRA/McGraw-Hill

Columbus, Ohio

Cover, Back Cover, Bruce Rowell/Masterfile

SRA/McGraw-Hill

*A Division of The **McGraw·Hill** Companies*

Send all inquiries to:
    SRA/McGraw-Hill
    8787 Orion Place
    Columbus, OH 43240-4027

ISBN 0-02-687941-7

    11 WAL 05

To the Teacher

PURPOSE:

USING THE CONTEXT has been designed to improve word comprehension and consequently comprehension in general. The reader's attention is directed to language patterns, word form, precise word usage, grammatical correctness, and word recognition. Most important of all, USING THE CONTEXT puts a premium on precise thinking.

FOR WHOM:

The skill of USING THE CONTEXT is developed through a series of books spanning ten levels (Picture, Preparatory, A, B, C, D, E, F, G, H). The Picture Level is for pupils who have not acquired a basic sight vocabulary. The Preparatory Level is for pupils who have a basic sight vocabulary but are not yet ready for the first-grade-level book. Books A through H are appropriate for pupils who can read on levels one through eight, respectively. **The use of the *Specific Skill Series Placement Test* is recommended to determine the appropriate level.**

THE NEW EDITION:

The fifth edition of the *Specific Skill Series* maintains the quality and focus that has distinguished this program for more than 25 years. A key element central to the program's success has been the unique nature of the reading selections. Nonfiction pieces about current topics have been designed to stimulate the interest of students, motivating them to use the comprehension strategies they have learned to further their reading. To keep this important aspect of the program intact, a percentage of the reading selections have been replaced in order to ensure the continued relevance of the subject material.

In addition, a significant percentage of the artwork in the program has been replaced to give the books a contemporary look. The cover photographs are designed to appeal to readers of all ages.

SESSIONS:

Short practice sessions are the most effective. It is desirable to have a practice session every day or every other day, using a few units each session.

SCORING:

Pupils should record their answers on the reproducible worksheets. The worksheets make scoring easier and provide uniform records of the pupils' work. Using worksheets also avoids consuming the exercise books.

To the Teacher

It is important for pupils to know how well they are doing. For this reason, units should be scored as soon as they have been completed. Then a discussion can be held in which pupils justify their choices. (The Integrated Language Activities, many of which are open-ended, do not lend themselves to an objective score; thus there are no answer keys for these pages.)

GENERAL INFORMATION ON *USING THE CONTEXT*:

The meaning of the word *context* should be explained at the outset of instruction. At the earlier reading levels pupils should think of *context* as meaning the *neighborhood* in which a word lives. They should think of it as a clue in identifying new words. This concept can be expanded until the reader conceives of *context* in the fullest sense of the term.

Pupils must understand that it is not desirable to sacrifice accuracy of comprehension for speed. Without rigid time limits, readers can judge each possibility against the total context.

SUGGESTED STEPS:

1. Pupils read the passage. As they come to a missing word, they substitute the word *blank* in its place and proceed until they finish the passage.
2. After pupils read the entire passage, they determine the best choices. If the answers are not immediately obvious, pupils should try each of the choices before making a decision. Common types of incorrect choices include **nonpertinent choice, restricted-context choice, imprecise choice, ungrammatical choice**, and **confused-form choice**.
3. On the Picture Level, pupils read the sentence first. Then they choose the picture that represents the word needed to complete the sentence.

Additional information on using USING THE CONTEXT with pupils will be found in the **Specific Skill Series Teacher's Manual**.

RELATED MATERIALS:

Specific Skill Series Placement Tests, which enable the teacher to place pupils at their appropriate levels in each skill, are available for the Elementary (Pre-1–6) and Midway (4–8) grade levels.

About This Book

How can you learn the meaning of a new word? One way is to use **context**. A word's context is the "neighborhood" in which a word "lives." A word comes in a sentence with other words. Other sentences come before and after the sentence with the new word. These words and sentences are the new word's context. A word's context gives clues to the word's meaning.

Try to figure out the meaning of the nonsense word in this sentence:

We will see bears and lions at the **dopp**.

If you guessed that a *dopp* is a *zoo*, you were right. You could figure that out from clues in the sentence like *bears* and *lions*. You used context clues to figure out the meaning of *dopp*.

In this book, you will read sets of sentences. In one sentence there is a blank. Under each set of sentences are three words. Pick the word that fits the blank. The context will help you decide which word is right.

"Here is a (1) _____ for you," said Tom. "Thank you," we all said at once.

1. (A) ball   **(B) jump**   **(C) how**

"Our cats like to (2) _____ milk," said the children. "They have milk every day."

2. (A) ask   **(B) laugh**   **(C) drink**

"I (3) _____ my coat," said Ann. "Will you help me find it?"

3. (A) ate   **(B) lost**   **(C) duck**

"Don't run so fast," we called. "You must (4) _____ down."

4. (A) slow   **(B) far**   **(C) but**

"I hope you can (5) _____ over to our house today. We could have fun," said my friend.

5. (A) last   **(B) story**   **(C) come**

"We called and called," said Bob, "but you didn't (6) _____ . Did you hear us?"

6. (A) after   **(B) cow**   **(C) come**

"May the (7) _____ of us go for a ride? May we ride to the city?" asked the children.

7. (A) three   **(B) give**   **(C) way**

A big red apple fell out of the tree. It (8) _____ down into the wagon.

8. (A) milk   **(B) said**   **(C) came**

"Please take (9) _____ and give it to the dog," said my friend. "Hear the dog bark for it!"

9. (A) say   **(B) this**   **(C) big**

My car will not go. I will take it to a woman who can make it (10) _____ .

10. (A) work   **(B) old**   **(C) dog**

Are there any (1) _____ in this water? They don't come to eat any more. Where did they go?

1. **(A) fish**   **(B) that**   **(C) good**

"Will you help?" asked Ann. "If you will help me a little, I can (2) _____ it."

2. **(A) first**   **(B) what**   **(C) do**

"How pretty the water is! This morning it looked green. Now it looks (3) _____ ," said Jan.

3. **(A) yes**   **(B) flower**   **(C) blue**

"Where (4) _____ you, Deb?" asked Tom. "I don't see you. Tell me where you are."

4. **(A) are**   **(B) let**   **(C) some**

Kim fell (5) _____ the water. Splash! "Help! I can't swim!" called Kim.

5. **(A) party**   **(B) up**   **(C) into**

Down the street (6) _____ Bob in his green wagon. Wes came after him in his yellow wagon.

6. (A) home   **(B) came**   **(C) me**

"This (7) _____ can go fast," said Ann. "But it can't go as fast as a car or an airplane."

7. (A) barn   **(B) boat**   **(C) little**

"Why not ask Jill and Kelly to come? We will have room for (8) _____ of them."

8. (A) both   **(B) dog**   **(C) very**

"Mother, guess what I saw at the zoo? A big brown (9) _____ was there!" said Pat.

9. (A) bear   **(B) shoe**   **(C) hurry**

"Please give me the box," said Tom. "I will put (10) _____ toys into it."

10. (A) after   **(B) thing**   **(C) our**

"I can't sleep," said Jan. "Help me get to sleep. It will (1) _____ be daylight."

1. (A) like   **(B) soon**   **(C) work**

"Let's (2) _____ your friend to the circus with us," said Father. "Would you like Bill to come?"

2. (A) make   **(B) take**   **(C) found**

The children looked up. The sky was very dark. Soon it (3) _____ to rain.

3. (A) began   **(B) said**   **(C) stop**

"When (4) _____ we eat dinner?" asked Tom. "I will help set the table."

4. (A) call   **(B) will**   **(C) very**

"Help! Help! The barn is on (5) _____ ! We must put it out," said Rosa.

5. (A) hill   **(B) open**   **(C) fire**

It was time to (6) _____ . Ann had a wagon, and Jim had his ball.

6. (A) play   **(B) fun**   **(C) to**

"I do not know what it is," said Bob. "But (7) _____ is in my room!"

7. (A) something   **(B) time**   **(C) took**

"We can give the kitten to Kim," said Ann. "She will take it to (8) _____ house."

8. (A) door   **(B) her**   **(C) look**

"What (9) _____ you do?" asked Father. "Tell me. Would you go by car or by airplane?"

9. (A) would   **(B) hat**   **(C) cold**

"No, Pat," said Mother. "I can't play (10) _____ with you now. Ask Jane to play."

10. (A) ask   **(B) fun**   **(C) ball**

We like this red (1)_____. May we go into it? Will we live here?

1. (A) some　　　　**(B) ride**　　　　**(C) house**

"It will take a long time for us to get there. They live (2)_____ away," said my friend.

2. (A) far　　　　**(B) next**　　　　**(C) let**

"The rain was a help," said Father. "Look at the grass. See how (3)_____ it is."

3. (A) red　　　　**(B) black**　　　　**(C) green**

"I am so hungry," said Deb. "I could eat all the (4)_____ in the house."

4. (A) books　　　　**(B) food**　　　　**(C) hills**

"No," said Mother. "They are not here. Look in the (5)_____ house. They may be there."

5. (A) tree　　　　**(B) money**　　　　**(C) sing**

"We went to the (6) _____," said Kelly. "We went to see the animals."

6. **(A) zoo** **(B) friend** **(C) there**

We took our pony to (7) _____ . All the children came out to see it.

7. **(A) new** **(B) school** **(C) on**

"Look behind the barn. You will see it," said my friend. "It's (8) _____ there."

8. **(A) draw** **(B) yes** **(C) over**

"You will have to (9) _____ . We want to be there on time," said Father.

9. **(A) hurry** **(B) sing** **(C) first**

The car came to a (10) _____ . We got in and went for a ride.

10. **(A) look** **(B) fish** **(C) stop**

A big bird sat on the tree by my window. It began to (1)_____.

1. (A) ran   (B) sing   (C) read

"Get out (2)_____ the wagon, Sam," said Tom. "I can't pull both of you."

2. (A) ball   (B) of   (C) today

The little black dog ran (3)_____. We could not find it. We looked and looked.

3. (A) said   (B) away   (C) please

"Do you know who lives (4)_____? It looks like a new house," said Mother.

4. (A) there   (B) say   (C) time

"We don't want that table," said Father. "It is (5)_____ big for just the three of us."

5. (A) soon   (B) went   (C) too

"Let's go to the farm," said my friend. "We can take a ride on the (6) _____ ."

6. (A) have   **(B) wagon**   **(C) away**

Down the (7) _____ we ran. You were first. Lee came next. I was last.

7. (A) fish   **(B) very**   **(C) hill**

"I wanted to play in the yard," said Sam. "But Mother (8) _____ me come into the house."

8. (A) made   **(B) zoo**   **(C) fast**

"Please buy me a little (9) _____ . I will keep it in the yard," said Jane.

9. (A) hat   **(B) birthday**   **(C) chicken**

"We will (10) _____ a house for the dog," said Father. "The dog is too big to live in our house."

10. (A) big   **(B) they**   **(C) build**

"I want to play more," said Jan. "Don't tell me it's going to (1) _____ !"

1. (A) said   **(B) rain**   **(C) run**

"Let's (2) _____ to the store," said Ron. "It is not very far from here."

2. (A) sing   **(B) walk**   **(C) then**

"Don't go into the (3) _____ now," said Mother. "It is too soon after your dinner."

3. (A) pretty   **(B) pull**   **(C) water**

The bed was (4) _____ big. It was too big for the little room Mary had.

4. (A) after   **(B) very**   **(C) find**

"Look at the barn. Let's go over to it. We will see who can get there (5) _____ ," said Bob.

5. (A) first   **(B) let**   **(C) catch**

"Look at that rabbit (6)＿＿＿＿＿!" called Jack. The rabbit was hopping away from the dog.

6. **(A) how**   **(B) hop**   **(C) her**

There were so many toys (7)＿＿＿＿＿ the store! I didn't know which one to buy.

7. **(A) in**   **(B) if**   **(C) sing**

"We can take a ride to the farm," said Mother. "We can get there (8)＿＿＿＿＿ dinner time."

8. **(A) eat**   **(B) work**   **(C) before**

Kelly looked in the barn. Joe looked in the yard. They could not find the (9)＿＿＿＿＿.

9. **(A) said**   **(B) hen**   **(C) slow**

"What (10)＿＿＿＿＿ of animal is that?" asked Ron. "It is a funny-looking animal."

10. **(A) kind**   **(B) draw**   **(C) wish**

A. Exercising Your Skill

When you read, you may see a word you do not know. How can you tell what this word means? One way is to look at the other words in the sentence and in nearby sentences. This is called using the **context**. Sometimes the words you *do* know will help you. Sometimes another word will have almost the same meaning as the new word. Sometimes the writer will tell you what the word means.

Read these sentences. Look for clues to the meanings of the underlined words. On your paper, write each underlined word. Then write what you think the word means. Tell what clues helped you figure out the meaning.

> Once, people thought dragons were everywhere. Some lived in the sky. Some <u>dwelt</u> in deep <u>caverns</u>, or caves. Some <u>resided</u> in rivers and lakes. The dragons watched over <u>treasures</u> of gold and money. They <u>protected</u> these things from people.

B. Expanding Your Skill

Could you tell that *lived*, *dwelt*, and *resided* all have the same meaning? Words that have almost the same meaning are called **synonyms**. Can you think of synonyms for other words in the sentences above? Write as many as you can. Look at your words. Then look at the words that others in your class wrote. Write down words that are new to you.

C. Exploring Language

Listen to this story. Some words will not sound right. Tell which words do not sound right. Give words that **will** sound right.

Dragons came in all sounds. There were green, red, blue, yellow, black, and white dragons. Some had wings. On their heads were horns, and their eyes had sharp nails. Some dragons were small. Others were as little as mountains.

Some people thought dragons could make rain. In wet times, farmers asked the dragons to send rain.

D. Expressing Yourself

Do one of these things.

1. Draw a picture of a scary dragon. Give your picture a name.

2. Some animals look like dragons. One animal that looks like a dragon is the lizard. Find a picture of an animal that you think looks like a dragon. Show the picture to your class. Tell why you think the animal looks like a dragon.

What is (1) _____ doing? She is looking for a new hat. She will buy the big hat she just tried on.

1. (A) Mother   **(B) Baby**   **(C) Father**

"Try not to (2) _____ too fast," said the teacher. "It does not sound right."

2. (A) funny   **(B) hill**   **(C) talk**

"What did the children (3) _____ ? Did they want to talk to me?" asked Father.

3. (A) say   **(B) duck**   **(C) with**

"I will be at home with my (4) _____," said Kelly. "Please call me there."

4. (A) making   **(B) family**   **(C) let**

The children liked the (5) _____ chicks. They played with them all day.

5. (A) yellow   **(B) swim**   **(C) cookies**

"You can't miss it," said Les. "Just look for the white (6) _____."

6. (A) **fast**   (B) **ride**   (C) **house**

"I wish I had a pet (7) _____," said Kim. "I would have fun with it."

7. (A) **city**   (B) **horse**   (C) **sleep**

"Mother and Father are home. I know they are there by now," (8) _____ Tom.

8. (A) **said**   (B) **stop**   (C) **door**

"Put the money (9) _____ it will not get lost," said Grandfather. "Put it here."

9. (A) **let**   (B) **where**   (C) **took**

"An old (10) _____ is under the water. It went down in the rain," said Juan.

10. (A) **boat**   (B) **smile**   (C) **new**

A fly is on the window. Put the window up. Maybe the fly will go (1) _____ .

1. (A) who　　　　**(B) was**　　　　**(C) out**

"I (2) _____ going to the picnic," said Ann. "So is Sam. All of us are going."

2. (A) am　　　　**(B) fell**　　　　**(C) hat**

"We must get there fast," said Pat. "We will go in a (3) _____ ."

3. (A) away　　　　**(B) car**　　　　**(C) something**

"Here they come! Oh, Bill, I think Father has our pet (4) _____ with him," said Kelly.

4. (A) cat　　　　**(B) rain**　　　　**(C) drink**

Bob said, "Please let me go for an (5) _____ ride. It will be fun."

5. (A) apple　　　　**(B) duck**　　　　**(C) airplane**

"Say (6) _____ to your father," Mother said. "He is going on the train."

6. (A) why   **(B) do**   **(C) good-by**

The children were (7) _____ . They said that they could go for a ride on the pony.

7. (A) happy   **(B) laugh**   **(C) if**

The farmer said, "This (8) _____ gives us all the milk we want."

8. (A) cow   **(B) umbrella**   **(C) cake**

"See if you can find the rabbit. It was in the garden last night," said Deb. "I (9) _____ to see it."

9. (A) name   **(B) pig**   **(C) want**

"There is only (10) _____ cookie here," said Sam. "You may have it, Kim."

10. (A) one   **(B) away**   **(C) race**

That road goes all around the city. It goes over (1) _____ and around water.

1. **(A) children**   **(B) hills**   **(C) people**

"Let's give Jane a (2) _____ for her birthday," said Lee. "We can play with it, too."

2. **(A) turtle**   **(B) hungry**   **(C) pull**

Tom took the duck to school. "It makes us laugh to see it walk," the children said. "It looks (3) _____ ."

3. **(A) funny**   **(B) has**   **(C) go**

Three horses came out of the barn. Two were black. The little one was (4) _____ .

4. **(A) store**   **(B) brown**   **(C) circus**

"I will write the letter for you. What do you want me to (5) _____ ?" asked my aunt.

5. **(A) boy**   **(B) give**   **(C) say**

"I will tell you a story," said Father. "After I do, it will be time to (6) _____ to sleep."

6. (A) then   **(B) but**   **(C) go**

"Put on your (7) _____ hats," said Mother. "We will go to see Grandmother and Grandfather."

7. (A) new   **(B) why**   **(C) laugh**

"I will make a cake," said Jan. "Will you (8) _____ me?"

8. (A) long   **(B) help**   **(C) after**

One of the children got the (9) _____ . Ms. Light began to read to the children.

9. (A) money   **(B) book**   **(C) went**

"Ask your school friends," said Deb. "They know how to sing it. They will (10) _____ us get to know it."

10. (A) help   **(B) look**   **(C) quack**

"Let me look at your (1) _____ ," said the teacher. "Something is in it. I'll get it out."

1. (A) far   **(B) eye**   **(C) ran**

"Well, well!" said Father. "What do you (2) _____ of your new toy airplane?"

2. (A) think   **(B) boat**   **(C) walk**

"Don't go (3) _____ out in the water," said Lee. "You may not get back."

3. (A) far   **(B) kitten**   **(C) stop**

I sat on the (4) _____ . Down the road I went. How happy I was!

4. (A) cake   **(B) pony**   **(C) baby**

"We cannot go there (5) _____ ," said Bob. "Please ask us again some day soon."

5. (A) today   **(B) began**   **(C) many**

We called and called, but no one came. Then, after a long (6) _____ , some friends came and helped us down from the tree.

6. (A) time   **(B) cake**   **(C) did**

The bird went up in the air. Soon it seemed small. Then we could (7) _____ see it at all.

7. (A) just   **(B) hop**   **(C) not**

It was a (8) _____ day for a ride. The grass was green and the water was blue.

8. (A) beautiful   **(B) city**   **(C) baby**

"Yes," said Mother. "The children were (9) _____ . They may go to the zoo."

9. (A) too   **(B) good**   **(C) road**

"Your friends are not here now. I will tell (10) _____ you were here," said Ann.

10. (A) them   **(B) your**   **(C) flower**

Some people (1) _____ our streets. Other people paint lines on the streets that tell cars where to go.

1. **(A)** clean   **(B)** laugh   **(C)** first

"Take the duck (2) _____ to the lake," said Pat. "Ducks like to play in water."

2. **(A)** many   **(B)** down   **(C)** come

"I don't know where they went," said Bob. "Did you (3) _____ to find out?"

3. **(A)** many   **(B)** try   **(C)** school

"Sam will be home before long," said Kim. "He will (4) _____ a surprise for us."

4. **(A)** baby   **(B)** soon   **(C)** have

"Let's (5) _____ here," said Matt. "Why not have our picnic by the water?"

5. **(A)** sit   **(B)** with   **(C)** never

The boys and girls ran after the (6) _____ , but it was too fast for them to catch.

6. **(A) up**   **(B) live**   **(C) pig**

Soon the (7) _____ will come to town. We will want to go, but will we have the money?

7. **(A) say**   **(B) circus**   **(C) wish**

"We live in a big (8) _____ ," said Jan. "You would have to come a long way to get here."

8. **(A) basket**   **(B) city**   **(C) walk**

All the children got into the car. They were happy. They began to (9) _____ .

9. **(A) sing**   **(B) find**   **(C) quack**

Meg painted a (10) _____ for me. I put it in my room.

10. **(A) keep**   **(B) picture**   **(C) show**

Ann likes to be in (1)＿＿＿＿. She likes to make people laugh and be happy.

1. (A) about　　　**(B) didn't**　　　**(C) shows**

"It is too (2)＿＿＿＿ for a swim. We can go some other day," said Tom.

2. (A) cold　　　**(B) fast**　　　**(C) slow**

"I see Pat and Lee. They are (3)＿＿＿＿! They have the rabbit with them!" said Bob.

3. (A) walk　　　**(B) coming**　　　**(C) fire**

Chickens live in a chicken house. At (4)＿＿＿＿ they all go into the house and go to sleep.

4. (A) green　　　**(B) night**　　　**(C) was**

"Did you (5)＿＿＿＿ me?" asked Jan. "Do you have something for me to do?"

5. (A) call　　　**(B) talk**　　　**(C) this**

"I am going to the picnic," said Sam. "Do you want to come (6) _____ me?"

6. (A) from　　　　**(B) with**　　　　**(C) had**

Tom opened the (7) _____ . What was in it? The children looked to see.

7. (A) box　　　　**(B) snow**　　　　**(C) walk**

"Mother was (8) _____ . We ran home from school today," said Maria.

8. (A) take　　　　**(B) book**　　　　**(C) surprised**

"Two of your friends may come to dinner," said Mother. "You may ask two of (9) _____ ."

9. (A) take　　　　**(B) again**　　　　**(C) them**

Many baby animals are like children. They like to play games (10) _____ .

10. (A) don't　　　　**(B) feet**　　　　**(C) too**

A. Exercising Your Skill

Some things go together. A cup and a glass go together. They have the same **context**. They are used for drinking. Can you think of any other things used for drinking?

The words in each group below go together in some way. They have the same context. Read each group of words. On your paper, write the name of one or two other things that belong in each group. Write a title, or name, for each group. Your title should tell the context of each group of words.

(Title)	*(Title)*	*(Title)*
stove	swing	pen
sink	slide	paper
pots	seesaw	pencil
____	____	____
____	____	____

B. Expanding Your Skill

Show your groups of words from Part A to your class. Talk about the words you wrote. Tell why you think the words go together. Tell why you picked the titles you gave your groups.

Did you and your class all write the same words? Write any new words on your paper.

C. Exploring Language

Draw a picture of some things that go together. Write a name for your picture. Then tell about these things. Write the sentences below on your paper. Then fill in the spaces. Give your story a title, or name.

_____(Title)_____

_____ , _____ , and _____ go together. You will find them in _____ . They go together because _____ _____ .

D. Expressing Yourself

Pick two or more things that go together. Then do one of these things.

1. Tell your class about the things. Tell how they go together.

2. Act out how these things are used. See if your class can guess what the things are.

"School ends at one (1)_____," said Ron. "After school, come and play at my house."

1. (A) where   **(B) today**   **(C) into**

"This morning we went to the farm," said Tom. "We saw a big (2)_____. It was a cow."

2. (A) little   **(B) please**   **(C) animal**

"What do I have?" asked Ann. "Don't look! Can you (3)_____ what I have?"

3. (A) guess   **(B) back**   **(C) would**

"I made a (4)_____ today," said Pat. "You may have some after you eat your dinner."

4. (A) keep   **(B) street**   **(C) pie**

"Did you (5)_____ Ron?" asked Father. "What do you say when someone gives you something?"

5. (A) sing   **(B) thank**   **(C) rain**

"No," we said, "you can't have this (6) _____ . It is for the party."

6. (A) pretty   (B) us   (C) cake

"I am hungry," said Matt. "May I have a big red (7) _____ to eat?"

7. (A) road   (B) apple   (C) barn

"I like you," said Kim. "You are good to me. You (8) _____ me a toy to play with."

8. (A) gave   (B) how   (C) stop

"Did you say you want a (9) _____ for a pet? What a funny pet that would make!" said Sam.

9. (A) find   (B) blue   (C) pig

"Let me give the (10) _____ some food. I think it is hungry," said Jan.

10. (A) kitten   (B) tree   (C) umbrella

The children have lost their dog. Its (1)_____ is Rover. It is brown with a white tail.

1. **(A) green**   **(B) hand**   **(C) name**

The black horse ran (2)_____ . It was very fast. They had to take the car to find it!

2. **(A) away**   **(B) don't**   **(C) pig**

Matt saw something black way (3)_____ in the tree. It was a big black cat.

3. **(A) up**   **(B) fun**   **(C) put**

"On what (4)_____ will you have the party? I will ask if I can come to it," said Pat.

4. **(A) nest**   **(B) day**   **(C) egg**

"Take the chicken you want. I will put (5)_____ into the basket," said the farmer.

5. **(A) it**   **(B) night**   **(C) rain**

"It will (6) _____ be night," said Lee. "It is time to go back home."

6. (A) soon   **(B) pet**   **(C) good**

___

Many of our friends went off to play ball. Some of us did (7) _____ go along.

7. (A) day   **(B) not**   **(C) my**

___

"We are not going by car," said Tom. "We must go (8) _____ our bus."

8. (A) little   **(B) feet**   **(C) with**

___

"It is there on the table," Mother said. "All you have to do is (9) _____ ."

9. (A) look   **(B) under**   **(C) again**

___

We asked, "Would you like to go for a (10) _____ in our boat?"

10. (A) good   **(B) before**   **(C) ride**

Sue will give her (1) _____ a new look. She will paint it blue and put up animal pictures.

1. (A) time   **(B) room**   **(C) face**

They found the ball (2) _____ the table. "So that is where it went!" I said.

2. (A) went   **(B) under**   **(C) catch**

"Will you help me (3) _____ my pennies? I lost two of them," said Ron.

3. (A) call   **(B) name**   **(C) find**

"Put the turtle back into the (4) _____ ," said Pat. "We do not want to take it home."

4. (A) after   **(B) miss**   **(C) water**

"I don't think I (5) _____ jump that far. It is over three feet," said José.

5. (A) can   **(B) show**   **(C) umbrella**

"Tell the (6) _____ to come back," said Father. "There are too many of them in the boat."

6. (A) children   (B) why   (C) day

"Please (7) _____ it to me," said Mother. "I will put it away for you."

7. (A) talk   (B) party   (C) give

"Will you help?" asked Bob. "Will you help me make my (8) _____ run?"

8. (A) get   (B) truck   (C) road

"You are in my way," said Ann. "I can't see the show. Please let me (9) _____ ."

9. (A) see   (B) never   (C) fish

"Tell us a (10) _____ , Deb. We want an animal story," said the children.

10. (A) soon   (B) coat   (C) story

All work and no (1)_____ is not good for you. You need some time for fun.

1. (A) **frog**   (B) **play**   (C) **look**

"The (2)_____ can't go fast," said Sam. "We can find it if we look."

2. (A) **turtle**   (B) **has**   (C) **of**

"Could you see (3)_____ in the boat? I was far out on the water," said Tom.

3. (A) **ride**   (B) **me**   (C) **after**

"We can have a (4)_____," said the children. "We will have it in the park."

4. (A) **far**   (B) **some**   (C) **party**

"You must not take that. It is not (5)_____ to play with," we said. "It is ours."

5. (A) **yours**   (B) **jump**   (C) **keep**

"Let's give them a (6) _____ ," said the farmer. "Would they like a horse?"

6. (A) the   (B) road   (C) pet

"You can be so (7) _____ ! You make all of us laugh," said Mother.

7. (A) funny   (B) many   (C) would

There were (8) _____ planes in the sky. They flew very low.

8. (A) eggs   (B) five   (C) trains

Ann took the toys (9) _____ of the box. "Here," she said. "Play with them."

9. (A) know   (B) began   (C) out

"Play out in the (10) _____ . Please do not run and play in here," said Mother.

10. (A) yard   (B) pretty   (C) began

Here comes the school (1) _____ . Ann and Bill will ride home on it.

1. (A) yes   **(B) bus**   **(C) but**

The children went (2) _____ one house to the next. They could not find the wagon.

2. (A) like   **(B) from**   **(C) thing**

"Our new (3) _____ is down the road," said Father. "We will get to see it today."

3. (A) blue   **(B) call**   **(C) house**

"Every time the cat went after the bird," said Deb, "the bird would (4) _____ away."

4. (A) friend   **(B) fly**   **(C) before**

"We were not very (5) _____ today. We can't go out and play," said Bob.

5. (A) ask   **(B) try**   **(C) good**

Grandfather (6) _____ on a hat. "Come, children," he said. "Let's take a walk."

6. (A) put   **(B) when**   **(C) don't**

"Kim is in school," said Mother. "She (7) _____ come out to play with you."

7. (A) blue   **(B) can't**   **(C) find**

"Go (8) _____ the others," said Tom. "We will all go fishing in our new boat."

8. (A) slow   **(B) get**   **(C) happy**

"It is time to stop playing," (9) _____ Mother. "It is time to feed your pets."

9. (A) home   **(B) help**   **(C) said**

Pat took Ann for a very fast ride. Ann (10) _____ out of the wagon!

10. (A) story   **(B) party**   **(C) fell**

Bill will (1)＿＿＿＿＿ down the big tree. Then he will have wood to use.

1. (A) cut   **(B) stop**   **(C) talk**

At the picnic there is (2)＿＿＿＿＿ to do all the time. There are games to play, and there is food to eat.

2. (A) ice   **(B) something**   **(C) school**

"Ask if you (3)＿＿＿＿＿ go," said the boys and girls. "We will be back soon."

3. (A) laugh   **(B) may**   **(C) before**

"A big (4)＿＿＿＿＿ has stopped out in the street," said Lee. "There is something for our house in it."

4. (A) sleep   **(B) please**   **(C) truck**

"We must get a (5)＿＿＿＿＿ car soon," said Ron. "Our car is getting too old."

5. (A) new   **(B) chicken**   **(C) rain**

Down the (6)_____ ran the horses! After them came Ann and Bob.

6. (A) road   **(B) many**   **(C) stop**

"Let's not go out (7)_____ the rain," said Jan. "When it stops, we can play."

7. (A) in   **(B) chicken**   **(C) from**

"It is time for work," said Kim. "We have had time for fun and (8)_____ all day."

8. (A) grow   **(B) play**   **(C) because**

"If you (9)_____ want to come," said Pat, "please tell me."

9. (A) boat   **(B) don't**   **(C) with**

"It's dark out (10)_____," said Sam. "I want to go into the house."

10. (A) doll   **(B) here**   **(C) or**

Ann was (1)＿＿＿＿＿ to school. It began to rain. Ann ran the rest of the way.

1. (A) cooking　　　**(B) walking**　　　**(C) sleeping**

"Tom (2)＿＿＿＿＿ not come to the party. He went away for the day," said Rosa.

2. (A) could　　　**(B) slow**　　　**(C) first**

"Please give me a (3)＿＿＿＿＿ to play with. I will give it back," said Bob.

3. (A) thank　　　**(B) laugh**　　　**(C) game**

We all looked in the big box. In it sat a little yellow (4)＿＿＿＿＿.

4. (A) grow　　　**(B) duck**　　　**(C) sleep**

"Come on (5)＿＿＿＿＿ now," said Ann. "You have been up there for a long time."

5. (A) table　　　**(B) my**　　　**(C) down**

Many trees were on fire. No one could (6) _____ .
Then the rain came. It put out the fire.

6. (A) pretty   **(B) at**   **(C) help**

"Thank you for the ride," said the children. "We
(7) _____ a good time."

7. (A) friend   **(B) had**   **(C) hello**

"Let's go to the (8) _____ ," said Kim. "I want to
see Grandmother and Grandfather."

8. (A) something   **(B) cat**   **(C) farm**

"Hello, Baby," said Sam. "Can you (9) _____ to
me? Say something."

9. (A) talk   **(B) away**   **(C) put**

"It is cold today," said Lee. "I will put on my hat and
(10) _____ ."

10. (A) horse   **(B) live**   **(C) coat**

A. Exercising Your Skill

Read this sentence. Think about ways you could end the sentence.

My pet is a _____ .

The word you pick has to sound right in the sentence. It has to fit the **context** of the sentence. That means it has to fit what the sentence is about. To end the sentence above, you need to write a word that names a kind of pet. On your paper, write the sentence. Use a word to end the sentence. Make sure that it sounds right in the sentence.

B. Expanding Your Skill

Share your new sentence with your class. How many different ways were there to end the sentence? The words should all have named different kinds of pets.

Did you name a pet that someone else named? What pet was named more than any other? Were there any kinds of pets you did not know? Ask your class to tell about these pets. You may want to write down new words you learned.

C. Exploring Language

Pick words from the box to finish the story. Remember that the word has to sound right in the sentence.

Most people ____ their pets. When some people die, they even leave ____ and other things to their pets. One woman left her pet turtle money so that he could go on having special ____ to eat. Another woman had a pet ____ named Blackie. When she died, she left money to buy a ____ for Blackie to live in. She also left money for ____ to take care of him.

cat	house	love
money	people	food

D. Expressing Yourself

Do you have a pet? If you do not have one, is there a pet you would like to have? Do one of these things.

1. Draw a picture of your pet. Give your pet a name. Tell your class about your pet.

2. Think about the way your pet moves. Try to move in the same way. See if your class can guess what kind of pet you are.

A big box is a good place to (1)_____ toys. You can use a box for books or games too.

1. (A) found   **(B) put**   **(C) think**

"Get back, children," said Father. "I am going to (2)_____ a fire for our picnic."

2. (A) make   **(B) sing**   **(C) walk**

"Ann can get into the car first," said Mother. "Sam can go (3)_____. Tom will go last."

3. (A) fell   **(B) next**   **(C) why**

"Please, may I have (4)_____?" asked Ron. "I would like to have a little of your cake."

4. (A) fast   **(B) wagon**   **(C) some**

Kelly ran (5)_____ the little rabbit but did not catch it. The rabbit got away.

5. (A) after   **(B) animal**   **(C) read**

"Your (6) _____ called," said Deb. "They want you to come out and play."

6. (A) it   (B) friends   (C) jump

"Take your (7) _____ ," we said. "We do not have to get there so soon."

7. (A) find   (B) time   (C) way

"Why can't Pat go to (8) _____ now?" asked Bob. "Pat is five years old."

8. (A) big   (B) splash   (C) school

"There are so (9) _____ animals! I never saw some of them before," said Bob.

9. (A) would   (B) last   (C) many

"To play this (10) _____ ," said Lee, "you run and jump. Who wants to play?"

10. (A) pet   (B) road   (C) game

The children in our class get along well together. Our teacher says, "Let's all be good (1) _____ ."

1. (A) nights   (B) friends   (C) papers

Tom cannot (2) _____ as far as Kim. Kim cannot run as fast as Tom.

2. (A) jump   (B) next   (C) street

"My friend is (3) _____ to school," said Ann. "I hope we will read a new story today."

3. (A) happy   (B) same   (C) coming

"Tell us a story," said Deb. "Tell us about all the children who lived in this (4) _____ ."

4. (A) house   (B) try   (C) red

"I think your (5) _____ is Matt," said Sam. "Don't you live in a house down the street?"

5. (A) hello   (B) name   (C) basket

"I can't find my toy (6)_____," said Jan. "Look up in the tree," said Ron.

6. (A) birthday   (B) where   (C) airplane

"What are you (7)_____?" asked Ann. "Is it something for the birthday party?"

7. (A) found   (B) catch   (C) making

"I (8)_____ saw that animal before," said Sam. "It looks something like a dog."

8. (A) went   (B) never   (C) what

"There are (9)_____ three of you," said Deb. "Can you eat all this cake?"

9. (A) just   (B) saw   (C) night

"We will go the first thing in the (10)_____," said Mother. "We must get some sleep first."

10. (A) fire   (B) dinner   (C) morning

Ann threw the ball. Her (1) _____ barked and ran after it.

1. (A) own   **(B) color**   **(C) dog**

"Put the animals in the (2) _____ . It is too cold out here," said the farmer.

2. (A) ball   **(B) ride**   **(C) barn**

I did not know (3) _____ to get on the horse. "Please help me," I said.

3. (A) how   **(B) pig**   **(C) far**

"You can give the toy boat to the baby," said Jan. "Please give the (4) _____ to me."

4. (A) what   **(B) away**   **(C) bike**

"Please do not (5) _____ the water on me," said Kim. "It is cold."

5. (A) splash   **(B) long**   **(C) box**

"Get the ball," said Pat. "It went under the (6)_____ ."

6. (A) time   **(B) chair**   **(C) had**

"I don't know (7)_____ they went away," said Bob. "But I know they will come back again."

7. (A) why   **(B) guess**   **(C) town**

"I could not find your house," said Ann. "On (8)_____ street is it?"

8. (A) food   **(B) which**   **(C) ask**

"Please eat your dinner (9)_____, Deb. It will get cold very soon," said Mother.

9. (A) horse   **(B) street**   **(C) now**

"Two of (10)_____ boys may go with me," said Father. "The girls may go with Mother."

10. (A) the   **(B) want**   **(C) have**

"I don't want to (1) _____," said Deb. "Why can't we eat now?"

1. **(A) they**   **(B) wait**   **(C) for**

"We will build a boat," said the children. "Then we (2) _____ take you all out on the water."

2. **(A) so**   **(B) will**   **(C) night**

"Please (3) _____ the others that we are going. They will want to know," said Lee.

3. **(A) back**   **(B) again**   **(C) tell**

"We had a very good time," said Ann. "Thank you for asking (4) _____ to the party."

4. **(A) us**   **(B) house**   **(C) car**

"The grass did not (5) _____ because it didn't rain," said Father.

5. **(A) play**   **(B) dinner**   **(C) grow**

The zoo is a (6) _____ for animals. Many animals live there.

6. (A) home   **(B) to**   **(C) make**

"Help the baby bird," said Deb. "Put it back up in (7) _____ tree."

7. (A) not   **(B) the**   **(C) too**

"I don't know where Jack went," said Dad. "I did not see (8) _____ today."

8. (A) her   **(B) him**   **(C) fell**

It was my birthday. My friends were coming to my party. How (9) _____ I was!

9. (A) happy   **(B) began**   **(C) talk**

"You can have all the (10) _____ you want. It is good for you," said Mother.

10. (A) little   **(B) barn**   **(C) milk**

The bird went (1) _____ into the water. It came up with a fish.

1. (A) up   **(B) down**   **(C) as**

"You (2) _____ not go out in the street. There are too many cars," said Maria.

2. (A) over   **(B) must**   **(C) work**

"They (3) _____ came back," said Mrs. Smith. "They are coming into the house now."

3. (A) yard   **(B) toy**   **(C) just**

"Is it time to eat?" asked Kelly. "We have played ball for a (4) _____ time."

4. (A) pig   **(B) long**   **(C) under**

"Look out in the garden," said Dad. "That is where I (5) _____ your rabbit."

5. (A) and   **(B) way**   **(C) saw**

Bob could find no (6) _____ at home. Where had they all gone?

6. (A) one   **(B) she**   **(C) take**

From the airplane Pat could (7) _____ cars and houses. They looked like little toys.

7. (A) want   **(B) see**   **(C) away**

"Let's go out to the farm," said Ann. "They have some new baby (8) _____ there."

8. (A) pigs   **(B) in**   **(C) ride**

"Let's put away our toys," said Deb. "It is time to go in and (9) _____."

9. (A) pony   **(B) fast**   **(C) eat**

"May the dog come into the house?" asked Jan. "It is raining out. Please (10) _____ the dog come in."

10. (A) what   **(B) let**   **(C) foot**

The water looks green and blue. There are many
(1) _____ out on it today.

1. (A) bears   **(B) nights**   **(C) boats**

"We will have (2) _____ at the party," said the
children. "I wish we were there now."

2. (A) next   **(B) fun**   **(C) way**

"Don't go back to sleep," said Grandmother. "This is a
big day. It is your (3) _____ ."

3. (A) birthday   **(B) had**   **(C) when**

"Let us go and see (4) _____ ," said Bob. "She
would like to see us."

4. (A) room   **(B) cake**   **(C) Grandmother**

"Kim and I like your pony. May we (5) _____ it?"
asked José.

5. (A) animal   **(B) ride**   **(C) at**

"You and Joe get into the car," said Mother. "We will (6) _____ Father to the train."

6. (A) many   **(B) take**   **(C) pet**

"There is room for (7) _____ girl and boy. All of you can come with us," said Father.

7. (A) every   **(B) over**   **(C) because**

"This is a (8) _____ story," said Ann. "We will read it after we eat."

8. (A) then   **(B) us**   **(C) good**

"Take the cow to the green (9) _____ ," said the farmer. "It does not have to stay in the barn."

9. (A) with   **(B) grass**   **(C) tell**

"Please keep the (10) _____ closed," said Grandmother. "It is cold out today."

10. (A) door   **(B) good**   **(C) splash**

A. Exercising Your Skill

You can use **context** to learn new words. When you find a word you do not know, look at the words around it. The other words can help you guess what the word means.

You can also use context to have fun with silly words! Read this sentence. Find the silly word. Then write the sentence on your paper. Use a word that sounds right in place of the silly word.

The nargle flew to its nest.

B. Expanding Your Skill

Did you use the word *bird* in place of *nargle*? What context clues helped you? Talk to your class about the clues you used. Then read these sentences. On your paper, write each sentence, using a word that sounds right in place of the silly word.

1. In blim, we learn how to read.
2. The glank shines high in the sky at noon.
3. My pet smiff barks at cats.
4. We flew in a zarb from New York to Florida.
5. Jerry and Chris are my best wunkles.

C. Exploring Language

Read this story. Use context clues to find the meanings of the underlined words. On your paper, write each word and its meaning.

Timmy and Tammy live in the <u>future</u> many years from now. In their city, everyone has a <u>vehicle</u> to fly. Timmy and Tammy like to fly their spaceship to the moon. The moon is <u>airless</u> and cold. But Timmy and Tammy don't care. They wear special <u>garments</u> to keep them warm. These spacesuits hold air for them to <u>breathe</u>, too.

Now write a sentence using one of the underlined words.

D. Expressing Yourself

Do one of these things.

1. Draw a picture about the sentence you wrote in Part C. Show your picture to your class and read your sentence to them.

2. Act out for your class what it might be like to be in a spaceship that is taking off to go to the moon. Talk about what it feels like.

3. Name as many words as you can that have to do with space. Try to name five words or more.